Disney · PIXAR

INCREDIBLES 2

Level 4

Re-told by: Jacquie Bloese
Series Editor: Rachel Wilson

Pearson Education Limited
KAO Two
KAO Park, Harlow,
Essex, CMI7 9NA, England
and Associated Companies throughout the world.

ISBN: 978-1-2923-4685-4

This edition first published by Pearson Education Ltd 2020

1 3 5 7 9 10 8 6 4 2

Set in Heinemann Roman Special, 14pt/23pt
Printed by Neografia, Slovakia

Published by Pearson Education Limited

Acknowledgments
Getty Images: Just_Super 26, metamorworks 26
Shutterstock.com: metamorworks 27

For a complete list of the titles available in the Pearson English Readers series, visit
www.pearsonenglishreaders.com.

Alternatively, write to your local Pearson Education office or
to Pearson English Readers Marketing Department,
Pearson Education, KAO Two, KAO Park, Harlow, Essex, CMI7 9NA

In This Book

Helen Parr / Elastigirl

Mom of the Parr family and a Super

Bob Parr / Mr. Incredible

Dad of the Parr family and a Super

Violet Parr

Dash and Jack-Jack's older sister

Dash Parr

Violet and Jack-Jack's brother

Jack-Jack Parr

The baby of the family

Winston Deavor

A rich and important man who loves Supers

Evelyn Deavor

A smart scientist and Winston's sister

Before You Read

Introduction

Supers are illegal now and Mr. Incredible and Elastigirl don't have jobs. Then they meet Winston Deavor and his sister, Evelyn. They love Supers and they want to work with the Incredibles. But who is the Screenslaver and can the Incredibles catch him? And who is going to stay home and watch the children …?

Activities

1 Look at page 17. Match the Supers with their powers.

1 Mr. Incredible

2 Elastigirl

3 Frozone

a can make ice and snow

b is very strong

c can stretch

2 Why are Supers illegal? Which of these reasons could be correct?

1 Because people don't understand them.

2 Because they don't work with the police.

3 Because they don't work hard.

4 Because sometimes they destroy city buildings and make a mess.

It was a dangerous time for the city. A very bad Super wanted to steal money from the banks. He destroyed a lot of buildings and took a lot of money.

The Incredibles and Frozone worked hard to stop the Super. But they didn't catch him and now the city was a mess.

The police weren't happy. The Supers always made a mess of
the city—and more problems for the police. That's why they
were illegal.

"We didn't start this fight," said Mr. Incredible.

"And you didn't finish it!" said the police officer angrily.

Mr. Incredible and Elastigirl went home. Now they had
no work.

Winston Deavor was an important man and he loved Supers. Mr. Incredible, Elastigirl, and Frozone met Winston and his sister, Evelyn.

"We must show your work to the world. Then Supers can be legal again," said Winston.

"How do we do that?" Elastigirl asked.

"With cameras," said Evelyn. "We build them into your Supersuits."

"We'd like to work with Elastigirl first," said Winston.

Bob and Helen went home. Helen thought a lot about Winston Deavor's plan.

"I don't know. It's nice to be wanted," she said to Bob, "but can I *really* leave the family right now?"

"I can watch the children," Bob said. "Easy. You go. You're going to be great!"

Helen smiled. Then she called Winston, "This is Elastigirl. I'm in."

The next day, the Parr family moved into a big house. It had a swimming pool and the children loved it.

"This is cool!" said Dash.

There was a present for Helen from Winston. It was an Elasticycle for her first job, and a new Supersuit. Helen was excited.

"You're going to be fine," she said to Bob. "Bye!"

The Elasticycle was very cool—it went really fast! Elastigirl met Winston and Evelyn.

"You're going to go to New Urbem," Winston told her.

In New Urbem, people were excited. There was a new train. It left the station, but it went the wrong way. The people on the train were really scared. Elastigirl started to chase it.

She raced through the city on her Elasticycle and jumped from building to building. The train went faster and faster. Then she jumped on top of the train, but her Elasticycle crashed. Elastigirl stretched into a parachute and slowly the train stopped.

Elastigirl went inside the train. The driver was hypnotized. Then a message came on his screen.

WELCOME BACK, ELASTIGIRL.

—THE SCREENSLAVER

Bob was at home with the children. Violet planned to go to the movies.

"I want you back here by ten-thirty," her dad said.

Bob read a story to Jack-Jack and the baby fell asleep.

Then he tried to help Dash with his schoolwork. Bob couldn't do it!

Now Bob was tired. He closed his eyes …

Bob woke up. He heard a noise outside. Jack-Jack was in the garden … with an animal! Light came from Jack-Jack's eyes. Then there were five Jack-Jacks! Bob tried to catch all of them.

"You … have … POWERS!" Bob was very excited.

Then Helen called. "How's the family? Do you want me to come back?"

"No. We're all … fine," said Bob looking at Jack-Jack.

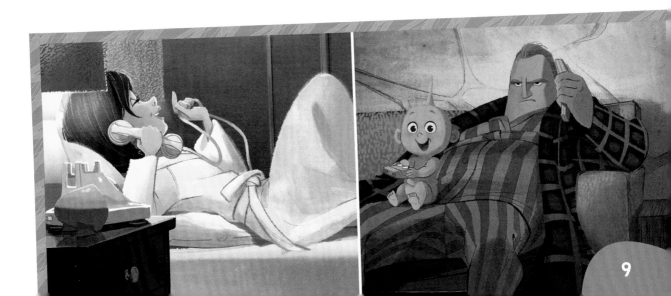

Elastigirl was on television. She talked to the TV man about the train. Suddenly, he started to speak strangely.

"I am the Screenslaver! I control your screens. Ambassador Selick's helicopter is going to crash."

Elastigirl jumped out of the window and went to the top of the building. Above her, there were three helicopters. Elastigirl broke the drivers' screens. Then she saved Ambassador Selick.

Elastigirl had to find the Screenslaver. Evelyn gave her
a tracker. The tracker took her to a building. It was the
Screenslaver's home! Elastigirl chased the Screenslaver but
he ran on top of the building. Then he jumped! But Elastigirl
caught him in her parachute.
Elastigirl took off his glasses. A young man looked back
at her. "What happened?" he said.

Back at home, Bob was very, very tired.

"Being a parent is hard," he thought. "I couldn't help Dash with his schoolwork. And what am I going to do about Jack-Jack? I ... I ..."

He spoke to Violet. "I want to be a good dad," he said.

Violet felt sorry for him. "You're not good ..." she said, "you're Super." But Bob was asleep!

Winston had a big party. "Thanks to Elastigirl, Supers are legal again!" he said.

Then Elastigirl saw the big screen, "Why is the film from my Supersuit on the screen in the Screenslaver's home?" she thought. "How could this happen?" she asked Evelyn. Elastigirl looked at the Screenslaver's glasses again. They had screens in them! Suddenly, Evelyn pushed Elastigirl and put the glasses on her.

Elastigirl woke up in a very cold room. Evelyn was there.

"You're the Screenslaver!" Elastigirl said. "But why?"

"People can do better without Supers," Evelyn said.
"Supers keep us weak!"

"Are you going to kill me?" Elastigirl was scared.

"No," Evelyn said. "Using you is better. You're going
to make Supers illegal again."

Evelyn called Bob. "Elastigirl wants you."

"What? What happened?" asked Bob.

"Meet me on our ship," said Evelyn."

On the ship, Mr. Incredible met Elastigirl. But Elastigirl started to fight him!

"Helen, it's *me*!" he said.

But she put the glasses on Mr. Incredible. Now he couldn't move.

A lot of Supers were on Winston's ship with Ambassador Selick and important people from different countries. They were there to make Supers legal again. People watched on their screens at home.

But then Evelyn hypnotized all the people in the room. "We don't want to help the world," the hypnotized Supers said. Evelyn controlled them. She told them to destroy the ship and crash into the city.

"We have to help Mom and Dad," Violet said to her brothers.
The Incredibile raced to the ship.
The Parr children arrived on the ship. They found their parents
and the other Supers. Jack-Jack took off his mom's glasses—
now she wasn't hypnotized. Then, Elastigirl took off Mr.
Incredible's glasses. The Incredibles were ready!

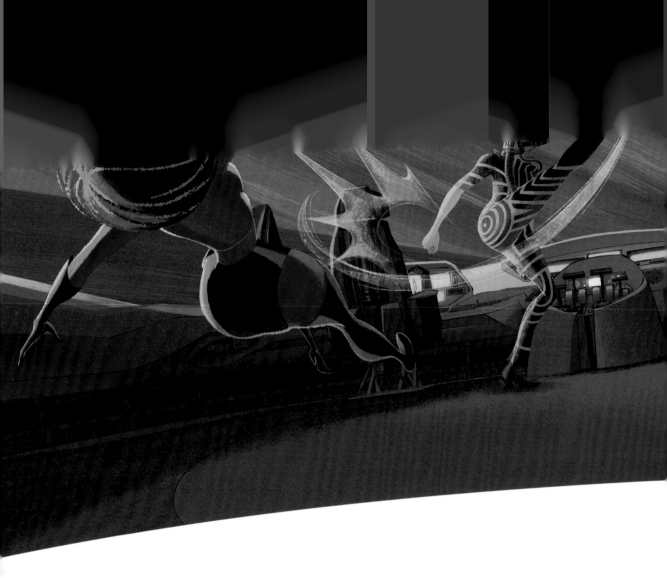

Evelyn tried to get away in a plane, but Elastigirl followed her. They fought hard.

"Supers are never going to be legal," Evelyn laughed. Then the window broke and Evelyn started to fall into the ocean. Elastigirl jumped out to save her. Voyd caught them—just in time! They were back on the ship.

"We have to stop the ship," said Frozone.

"What about turning it?" said Dash.

Mr. Incredible swam under the ship. Slowly, it began to turn away from the city. Frozone made a snow bridge between the ship and the city. The ship stopped and the city was safe. The police came and took Evelyn away.

Supers were legal again. The Parr family was really happy.

"Who wants to see a movie?" asked Bob.

"Yes!" the children shouted.

The Parr family drove through the city. Then a police car raced past … Perhaps the movie could wait. There was work to do—and the Incredibles were ready for it!

After You Read

1 **Read and say True or False.**

1 Winston Deavor loves Supers.

2 Bob doesn't want Helen to be a Super.

3 Jack-Jack has powers.

4 Evelyn is a good friend to Elastigirl.

5 Elastigirl saves the train in New Urbem.

2 **Look at the headlines. Put them into the correct order.**

a SUPERS ARE LEGAL AGAIN

b ALL SUPERS ARE ILLEGAL

c ELASTIGIRL STOPS TRAIN!

d A MESSAGE FROM THE SUPERS: WE WANT TO DESTROY THE WORLD!

e "I NEARLY DIED IN A HELICOPTER CRASH," SAYS AMBASSADOR SELICK

3 **Read the questions. Discuss with a friend.**

1 In the story, Bob watches the children and Elastigirl goes out to work. Which job is the most difficult, do you think? Why?

2 The Parr children come and help their parents on the ship. What does this tell us about the message of the story?

Glossary

camera (*noun*) you take photos with a camera

catch past tense **caught** (*verb*) to stop a person or thing that is moving; *But they didn't catch him and now the city was a mess.*

chase past tense **chased** (*verb*) to quickly follow and try to catch a person or thing; *Elastigirl chased the Screenslaver but he ran on top of the building.*

control past tense **controlled** (*verb*) to have the power to make a person or thing do what you want; *Evelyn controlled them.*

crash past tense **crashed** (*verb*) to have an accident; *Ambassador Selick's helicopter is going to crash.*

destroy past tense **destroyed** (*verb*) to break a thing; *She told them to destroy the ship and crash into the city.*

fight past tense **fought** (*verb*) to hit a person; *But Elastigirl started to fight him!*

helicopter (*noun*) helicopters can fly straight up, down, left, right, and back

hypnotize past tense **hypnotized** (*verb*) to put a person into a kind of sleep so that you can control them; *The driver was hypnotized.*

illegal (*adj.*) a thing that is not allowed; *Supers are illegal now and Mr. Incredible and Elastigirl don't have jobs.*

message (*noun*) we can write, send, and read messages from a computer or cell phone

parachute (*noun*) a parachute helps you fall safely through the sky

race past tense **raced** (*verb*) to run or drive quickly; *She raced through the city on her Elasticycle and jumped from building to building.*

safe (*adj.*) not in danger

screen (*noun*) a flat place on a computer, cell phone, or television that lets you see pictures or words

stretch past tense **stretched** (*verb*) to become bigger or longer; *Elastigirl stretched into a parachute and slowly the train stopped.*

Phonics

Say the sounds. Read the words.

scr

(screen)   (describe)

str

(stretch)   (strong)

Say the rhyme.

Elastigirl stretches and saves the train.
The city streets are safe again.

A strange message is on the screen.
Who's the Screenslaver and what does it mean?

Destroy the Supers—that's Evelyn's plan.
Who can help? The Incredibles can!

Values

Work hard.

Go and work for Winston. I can watch the children.

Bob worked hard at home.

The Frubbers of Freep are going to sleep …

Come with me, Ambassador!

Elastigirl worked hard in the city.

Violet and Dash helped, too.

Where's Jack-Jack? I have to find him.

I have to fight Voyd!

We're always ready to help!

Find Out

Are driverless cars the future?

What is a driverless car? A driverless car is a car with no person driving it. A computer is the driver!
A driverless car has sensors which "see" the other cars around it. Cameras in the car watch the road. The computer reads all the information and the car moves.

Why do people want driverless cars? Driverless cars are easy for people—you don't have to use maps or think about bad weather! You can sleep or work in the car. And they're great for older people who can't drive.

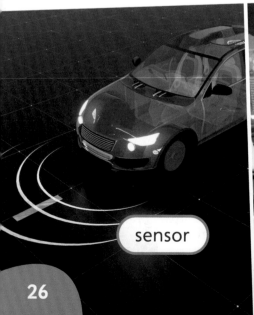

sensor

information

Self-Driving

Are driverless cars safe? They are safer than cars with drivers. A lot of car accidents happen because drivers are tired. Computers never sleep!

When can I travel in a driverless car? Engineers are testing driverless cars now. "Driverless cars must be 99.99% safe before people can use them," they say.

engineer (*noun*) a computer engineer builds computers
test (*verb*) engineers test computers before people buy them